I Am Kindness

A book about sharing kindness with everyone

Cachet Allen

DEDICATION

To my three beautiful children who are my light and
love. You inspire me everyday.
May you grow up in a world with peace and kindness.

To my mother who always believed in me and told me to
reach beyond the stars.

To my husband who always loves me unconditionally
and gives me endless support.

Dear Parents and Teachers,

By sharing and discussing this book with your children, you will be helping them learn how easy simple acts of kindness can be.

Kindness is being mindful about yourself, others and the things around you. There are so many different ways to show kindness:

Be kind with your thoughts.
Be Kind with your words.
Be kind with what you buy.
Be kind with what you wear.
Be kind with how you eat.
Be kind with how you treat the environment, animals, nature and each other.

All that you do can help make the world a little kinder.

Kindness is the
GREATEST
thing
you can share,

PASS IT ON
to a bug
or a grumpy old
bear.

HELP A FRIEND
out in need,
it's not hard to think.
A small gesture, a smile,
a hug or a wink.

It takes nothing at all to show
that you care.

So show your kindness to ALL
CREATURES everywhere.

Have COMPASSION for all
with two feet or four.

It creates JOY all around us,
we could use a lot more.

It's always good to share

Always smile

I'm kind to others and myself

Say NICE words,
give a hand,
or give
GOOD ADVICE.

I enjoy helping others

It's the
NICEST
thing
we can do
for each
other,

big or small, short or tall, towards your sisters and your brothers.

TRUE kindness comes
from a good
HEART and SOUL,

SHARE YOUR LOVE
with others whether you're
young or you're old.

You can be a **LEADER** and always show your **TRUE HEART**,

others will follow you once you start.

Kindness can be
CONTAGIOUS, that's a
good thing!

The WORLD
would be a
BETTER PLACE,

LOVE

PEACE

JOY

So get into the swing of LIFE and LOVE,
there's no holding you back,

just go with the flow
and stay on the
RIGHT TRACK.

Kindness is a CHOICE that you make.
So keep your heart W I D E O P E N

to GROW and GLOW and
FLOW with DEVOTION.

HAPPINESS

LIFE WILL REWARD YOU,
you will feel it through your
own HAPPINESS.

GOOD THINGS
will surround you,
It will be INSTANTANEOUS!

Remember the
POWER of
KINDNESS,
Compassion and
LOVE.

These are your
NATURAL GIFTS
that you should be
PROUD of.

I Am Kind.
I Am Kindness.

Kindness
JOY
Care
happiness

THESE ARE DIFFERENT WAYS TO EXPLAIN SOME OF THE WORDS

Kindness: to care, love or show goodness towards someone or something. To be sweet or patient. To be thoughtful.

Gesture: a kind offering.

Creatures: anything living, all animals, insects, plants. All nature.

Compassion: a deep or strong feeling for someone.

Advice: to help someone by offering help.

Contagious: to spread from person to person. Spread joy.

Choice: the power to choose what you want to do.

Devotion: to a have a strong feeling of love for something. Loyalty.

Reward: something given to you in return for something good that you've done.

Instantaneous: something that happens right away.

Integrity: goodness and honesty.

Respect: to treat highly, to be kind or appropriate. To show admiration.

ISBN 978-0-9959437-0-4 (Hardcover)

ISBN 978-0-9959437-1-1 (Paperback)

Printed and bound in Canada by Art Bookbindery
www.ArtBookbindery.com